A Banker's Confession

Study Guide

by Gary Sanseri

A Banker's Confession Study Guide
© 1992 by Gary Sanseri

Published by   Back Home Industries
               P.O. Box 22495
               Milwaukie, OR 97269

Printed in the United States of America

ISBN 1-880045-09-5

This study guide is designed to help you understand the benefits of debt free living in a credit card society and other concepts presented in Banker's Confession to the end that Jesus Christ be glorified.

The wicked borrows and does not repay,
But the righteous shows mercy and gives.

--Psalm 37: 21

The rich rules over the poor,
And the borrower is servant to the lender.

--Proverbs 22:7

Banker's Confession Study Questions

Chapter 1: My Personal Struggle with Debt

1.   How much money can a family with a $100,000 loan at 10.5% for 30 years save by simply prepaying an additional $30 a month?

How much sooner will they pay off the loan?

2.   Why don't banks recommend prepayments? Explain.

3.   What assumptions did Gary and his wife make when they bought their home?

.   What desire was restricted for Gary because of the debt on his home?

4.   What happened when Gary and his wife pre-paid their mortgage?

5.   How has real estate been effected by the economic crisis in our country?

6.   Define leverage (p. 16).

7.   List faulty presumptions about leverage.

    1.

    2.

    3.

    4.

8. Which group of people will be the first to suffer financial ruin in times of recession or depression? Explain why.

Banker's Confession Study Questions

Chapter 2: We Owe It to Ourselves

1.   What problems did our country experience under George Washington when the national debt accumulated? (pgs. 19-21)

2.   What happened when Congress attempted to finance the Revolutionary War debt through issuing paper money? (pages 21-22)

3.   How much did the Continental dollar depreciate from the time of printing in 1775 until January 14, 1779? (In other words an item that would have cost one dollar in 1775, would cost how much four years later?)

How much did the Continental dollar depreciate in eight months (by Sept. of 1779)?

How much did the Continental dollar depreciate by January 1781?

4.   From your own observations, can you identify similarities to what is happening today in this country?

5.   From the chart on page 23, how much did the federal deficit grow between1885 and 1985?

6.   What two written notes about finances were found in the pocket of the Honorable Stephen Allen when he died?

    1.

    2.

7.   What is wrong with the idea, "We owe it to ourselves?"

8.   Paraphrase (resay in your own words) Washington's ideas on the sacred regard to public justice.

Banker's Confession Study Questions

Chapter 3: The Enslaving Power of Debt

1.   How did the telephone advertisement lure the consumer into making a $109.80 purchase?

2.   Purchasing a home on time is more costly than the phone purchase because of the added interest charges. How much extra would the homeowner described on page 30 pay for his home because of interest payments?

3.   How does modern thinking conflict with Proverbs 22:7?

4.   Define debt.

5.   Explain the statement, "Some sell their liberty to gratify their luxury."

6.   Read the story of Onesimus in the book of Philemon.

Define the LORD's freedman.

Define the LORD's slave.

7.   How can earthly entanglements restrict our service to God?

8.   What was George Whitefield's experience with debt? What wrong action did he take in order to help pay off his debts?

Banker's Confession Study Questions

Chapter 4:   Other Hazards of Debt

1.   How much did Samuel Wesley's income
increase by his job change?   _____lbs.

How much money did he borrow against
predicted income to buy furniture
and farm tools needed by the move?   - _____lbs.

balance (not counting interest)   _____lbs.

How much did barn repairs cost?   - _____ lbs.

balance remaining   _____lbs.

How much did Samuel's mother need to
hold off creditors   - _____lbs.

balance remaining   _____lbs.

How much did Samuel owe the government
because of his new increased salary
      First Fruits Tax   _____lbs.
      John of Jerusalem Tax   _____lbs.
      tithe   +_____lbs.
total debt over ability to pay   _____ lbs.

What were the consequences of Wesley's financial debt?

2.   What percentage of their income does the average American churchgoer give to the Lord?

3.   What is God's response (Mal 3:8)?

4.   How does debt cause us to rob God by neglecting the poor?

5.   How would obedience to the principle in Hebrews 13:5 help protect us from the pitfalls of debt spending?

6.   On a separate sheet of paper list the six ways of reaching contentment identified by John MacArthur:

7.   How did greed bring ruin to Robert Morris, a once generous man?

8.   Define presumption and explain how it relates to debt.

Banker's Confession Study Questions

Chapter 5: The History of Usury:
Part One
Ancient Times to Christ

1.   The story of the Pilgrims illusrates how debt with usury equals extended servitude. How much did the Pilgrims pay in interest on the $1800 pounds they borrowed?

2.   Define: wealth

       usury

       money

3.   How did the Israelites differ from the Gentiles in financial matters?

4.   Were the Israelites supposed to charge interest to brothers (Lev 25:35-38, Deuteronomy 23:19; Nehemiah 5:1-13)?

Was it wrong for Israelites to charge usury to foreigners (Deut. 23:20)? What do you feel is the reason for the different standard?

5.   Why, according to Tom Rose, are people willing to pay interest (p. 62-63)?

6.   Name some of the prophets and philosophers of the Ancient World who denounced usury. Explain their reasons for disliking the practice.

7.   Although the philosophers denounced the exacting of usury, what actually took place in ancient Greece and Rome? What were the consequences of such practices?

8.   What was Christ's attitude toward loaning to the poor? Be sure to discuss the pertinent scriptures to defend your conclusion.

Banker's Confession Study Questions

Chapter 6: The History of Usury:
Part Two
The Early Church to Modern Times

1.   Summarize Charles Spurgeon's attitude toward debt.

2.   What foundation did the first century church lay regarding a Christian view of helping the poor?

3.   Identify Tertullian. What did he teach about usury?

4.   What important change began to take place among Christians during the rule of Constantine?

What important council was called in 325 A.D.? Why?

What was its decision regarding usury?

5.   What were these men's belief on usury?

Basil

Augustine

6.   What compromise took place in the early days of the Reformation which changed the entire outlook on usury?

How did both Luther and Calvin view usury?

7.   What important change in terminology took place in Calvin's day?

What did the English philosopher, David Hume, say about this change?

How does this change affect us today?

8   How did the Puritans view the taking of interest? What type of thinking has affected modern society the most regarding the taking of interest? What is the outlook for the future?

Banker's Confession Study Questions

Chapter 7:   The Marvel of Loan Pre-Payment

1.   Before purchasing a home one should always count the cost. Including interest how much will Jake and Sue make in payments for their house?

What are some expenses involved in home ownership in addition to the monthly mortgage?

Ask someone how much they pay a year in house insurance and property taxes.

2. Define pre-payment.

3. Complete the chart below using information in Jake and Sue's situation described on page 97.

monthly pre-payment	cost of loan	amt.saved	years reduced from loan
0	$183,565	0	0
$26	$146,750*	$36,815	5
$74	_____	_____	____
167	_____	_____	____

* $183,565 - 36,815 = $ 146,750

13

4.   a.   Explain the constant prepayment plan.

      b.   According to the chart on page 98, how much would one save with a $50 a month prepayment?

      c.   Use the amortization schedules in the appendix of the Banker's Confession beginning on page 175 to complete the following chart. Note: Look on page 192 for the information on the $25 prepayment. The statement at the beginning (on page 185) only reflects the original loan. Savings are determined by studying the end of each schedule. Subtract the total interest from $161,214.52 to determine total savings.

prepayment amount	number of payments	total interest	total savings
0	360	$161,214.52	0
25	308	$132,748.99	____
50	____	____	____
100	____	____	____
200	____	____	____

5.   Explain shifting and periodic payment plans.

6.   Explain the idea of paying the next months principal in advance.

According to table 5 how much would one spend in prepayments to save $3812.13?

7.   What is the advantage of bi-weekly scheduled payments.

How much would be saved in interest for a $85,000 loan at 9% interest if paid bi-monthly?

8.   How would you answer the person who is hesitant to make pre-payments because of a supposed loss of a tax advantage?

Banker's Confession Study Questions

Chapter 8: The Value of Thrift

1.   What three economic principles did John D. Rockefeller learn from the beginning?

    1. to_____

    2. to_____

    3. to _____

2. Richard Cobden divides the world into what 2 classes?

    1.

    2.

    Which class contributes the most to society and why?

3.   What lesson can we learn from the story Mr. Budgett, his servant girl and a potato?

4.   What did John Maynard Keynes consider as economic virtues?

What did he construe as vices to be avoided?

What has been the result of our nation following this man's advice?

5.   List some biblically based home business ideas for enhancing income inspired by Proverbs 31.

Can you think of others?

6.   Explain why a wife's job away from home often contributes little or no actual gain.

7.   How can using cash for puchases save money and protect you from the temptation to over spend?

8.   List and explain five or more additional ways to enhance income.

One neighbor acknowledged that it would be wonderful to own their home free and clear, but said they could never afford to do so. The next week her husband received a salary raise. They are now planning to move into a more expensive house. Which principle of income enhancement did they ignore?

Banker's Confession Study Questions

Chapter 9: Investing for the Future

1.   Read and report on R.G. LeTourneau's autobiography, <u>Mover of Men and Mountains</u>.

What was this man's motto?

How did God honor this man's faith?

2.   What are some advantages of self employment?

3.   Study the list of self-employment ideas on page 128. Can you think of at least five other areas?

4.   Interview at least one family, friend or neighbor who works out of their home. Ask them to give you several advantages and several disadvantages of their work situation. See if they have any advice which they wish someone had told them before they started.

5.   What is one of the greatest causes of business failure? Explain.

6.   List six or more other possibilities for investment.

7.   Paraphrase Deuteronomy 14:29.

8.   Why is giving listed as a type of investment. (See Deuteronomy 15:10; 2 Cor 9:6-7.)

Additional Resources from Back Home Industries

Qty	Title	Amt
_____	A Banker's Confession @ $9.95	_____
_____	Advent Foretold @ $14.95	_____
_____	God's Priceless Woman @ $19.95	_____
_____	The New England Primer @ $14.95	_____
_____	Moody's Child Stories @ $17.95	_____
_____	Teaching Reading at Home @ $19.95	_____
_____	Phonogram Cards @ $12.95	_____
_____	Phonogram Tapes @ $5.95	_____
_____	Free Catalog	
	Shipping (10% Minimum $2.50)	_____
	Total	_____

Send to: **Back Home Industries**
P.O. Box 22495, Milwaukie, OR 97269

From: Name_____

Address_____

City, State, Zip_____

ISBN 1-880045-09-5